PELEG TOP
MENTOR. ARTIST.

CREATIVE HIGH GROWTH

Journal

good
juju
PUBLISHING

all is full
of love

Dear Voyager,

This book is dedicated
to your inner artist.

Guidance and direction for
your journey are in these pages.

Let your soul speak.

Let your heart lead.

Let your words create.

Abracadabra, Lover!

Divine Love,

Allow me to give with complete ease and abundance, knowing that You are the unlimited Source of all.

Let me be an easy, open conduit for Your prosperity.

Let me trust that all my own needs are always met in amazing ways and that it's safe to give freely as my heart guides.

And equally, let me feel wildly open to receiving.

May I know my own value, beauty, and worthiness without question.

Let me allow others the supreme pleasure of giving to me.

May I feel worthy to receive in every possible way.

Change me into one who can fully love, forgive, and accept myself so I may carry love without restriction.

Let everything that needs to go, go.

Let everything that needs to come, come.

I am utterly Your own.

You are me, I am You, we are One.

All is well and all is full of love.

Made in the USA
Middletown, DE
25 April 2022

64735115R00170